Theory Paper Grade 6   2008   A

Duration 3 hours

Candidates should answer all FIVE questions.
Write your answers on this paper – no others will be accepted.
Answers must be written clearly and neatly – otherwise marks may be lost.

1 Answer **ONE** section only, (a) or (b).

15

EITHER

(a) Indicate **ONE** chord at each of the places marked * to accompany the following melody. You may do so by writing roman numerals or any other recognized method of notation between the staves, **OR** by writing notes on the staves which provide a proper harmonic structure; but use only **ONE** of these methods.

[Moderato]

Melody by J. Clark (adapted)

3

OR

(b) Complete the bass line and add a suitable figured bass as necessary, *from the first beat of bar 2*, at the places marked * in this passage. If you wish to use a ⁵₃ chord, leave the space under the asterisk blank, but ⁵₃ chords *must* be shown when used as part of a ⁶₄ ⁵₃ progression or when chromatic alteration is required.

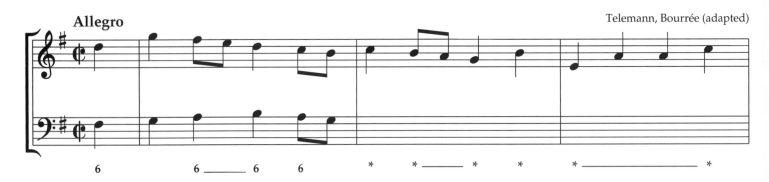

2 Writing for four-part voices (SATB) or keyboard, realize this figured bass. Assume that all chords are ⁵₃ unless otherwise shown.

3 EITHER

(a) Continue this opening to form a complete melody for unaccompanied flute. It should end with a modulation to the subdominant and should be between eight and ten bars long. Add performance directions as appropriate and write the complete melody on the staves below.

OR

(b) Continue this opening for unaccompanied oboe to make a complete piece of not less than eight bars in length. You may make any modulation or modulations that you wish, or none if you prefer. Add performance directions as appropriate and write the complete melody on the staves below.

attacca subito

4 Look at the extract from a piano piece, printed opposite, and then answer the questions below. [25]

(a) Give the meaning of *attacca subito* (bar 21).

.... (2)

(b) Identify the chords marked * in bars 7 and 20 by writing on the dotted lines below. Use either words or symbols. For each chord, indicate the position, show whether it is major, minor, augmented or diminished, and name the prevailing key.

Bar 7 .... Key .... (4)

Bar 20 .... Key .... (4)

(c) Mark **clearly** on the score, using the appropriate capital letter for identification, one example of each of the following. Also give the bar number(s) of each of your answers, as shown in the answer to **A**.

In bars 1–8

A an imperfect cadence in the tonic key. Bar ......4......

B an example of syncopation in the right-hand part. Bar .... (2)

C a note of anticipation (circle the note concerned). Bar .... (2)

D a dominant inner pedal (not sustained) lasting
for four bars (mark ⌐   D   ¬ over the bars). Bars .... (2)

From bar 9 onwards

E a melodic interval of a diminished 8ve in the
right-hand part (circle the notes concerned). Bar .... (2)

F a chromatic accented passing note over
tonic harmony (circle the note concerned). Bar .... (2)

(d) Write out in full the right-hand part of bar 1 as you think it should be played.

(3)

(e) From the following list, underline the name of the most likely composer of this piece, and give a reason for your answer.

Debussy   Bach   Mozart   Chopin   (1)

Reason: ....

.... (1)

7

5 Look at the extract printed on pages 9–10, which is taken from Fauré's *Masques et bergamasques*, and then answer the questions below.

(a) Give the meaning of:

molto vivo .... (2)

a 2 (bar 7, bassoons) .... (2)

𝅘𝅥 (e.g. bar 1, second violins) .... (2)

(b) (i) Write out the parts for horns in bars 5–7 as they would sound at concert pitch and using the given clef.

(3)

(ii) Using the blank stave on page 10, write out the parts for clarinets in bars 12–15 as they would sound at concert pitch. (4)

(c) Describe fully the numbered and bracketed harmonic intervals *sounding* between:

1 first bassoon and violas, bar 6, first crotchet .... (2)

2 double bass and second horn, bar 8, first crotchet .... (2)

3 bassoons and cellos, bar 9, fourth crotchet .... (2)

(d) Answer TRUE or FALSE to each of the following statements:

(i) The double basses are played arco throughout the extract. .... (2)

(ii) The chord *sounding* on the last crotchet of bar 7 is a supertonic 7th in first inversion (ii⁷b). .... (2)

(iii) The largest melodic interval in a string part is a perfect octave. .... (2)

etc.

(b)   (ii)

Clarinets, bars 12–15

etc.

Theory Paper Grade 6   2008   B

TOTAL MARKS
100

Duration 3 hours

Candidates should answer all FIVE questions.
Write your answers on this paper – no others will be accepted.
Answers must be written clearly and neatly – otherwise marks may be lost.

1   Answer ONE section only, (a) or (b).

15

EITHER

(a) Indicate ONE chord at each of the places marked * to accompany the following melody. You may do so by writing roman numerals or any other recognized method of notation between the staves, OR by writing notes on the staves which provide a proper harmonic structure; but use only ONE of these methods.

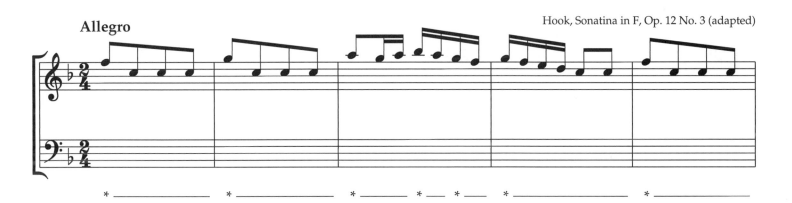

Allegro

Hook, Sonatina in F, Op. 12 No. 3 (adapted)

etc.

(b) Complete the bass line and add a suitable figured bass as necessary, *from the first beat of bar 4*, at the places marked * in this passage. If you wish to use a $\frac{5}{3}$ chord, leave the space under the asterisk blank, but $\frac{5}{3}$ chords *must* be shown when used as part of a $\frac{6}{4}\frac{5}{3}$ progression or when chromatic alteration is required.

Rameau, Menuet I (adapted)

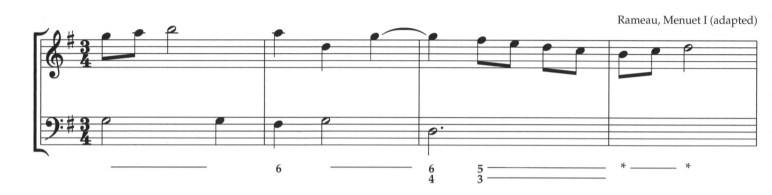

2 Writing for four-part voices (SATB) or keyboard, realize this figured bass.  Assume that all chords are $\frac{5}{3}$ unless otherwise shown.

3 EITHER

(a) Continue this opening to form a complete melody for unaccompanied cello. It should end with a modulation to the relative major and should be between eight and ten bars long. Add performance directions as appropriate and write the complete melody on the staves below.

Allegro   Mozart (adapted)

OR

(b) Continue this opening for unaccompanied flute to make a complete piece of not less than eight bars in length. You may make any modulation or modulations that you wish, or none if you prefer. Add performance directions as appropriate and write the complete melody on the staves below.

Allegretto

4 Look at the extract printed opposite, which is from a piece for violin and piano, and then answer the questions below. 25

(a) Identify the chords marked ∗ in bars 2 and 25 by writing on the dotted lines below. Use either words or symbols. For each chord, indicate the position, show whether it is major, minor, augmented or diminished, and name the prevailing key.

Bar 2 .... Key .... (4)

Bar 25 .... Key .... (4)

(b) Name two similarities and two differences between the two bracketed sections in bars 1–4 and 9–12.

Similarities 1 .... (1)

2 .... (1)

Differences 1 .... (1)

2 .... (1)

(c) Write out in full the violin part of bar 19 as you think it should be played.

(3)

(d) Give the full names of the notes of melodic decoration (e.g. note of anticipation) marked **X** and **Y** in bars 12 and 25.

X .... (2)

Y .... (2)

(e) Describe fully the following bracketed harmonic intervals in the violin part:

(i) bar 11 .... (2)

(ii) bar 30 (top and bottom notes) .... (2)

(f) From the following list, underline the name of the most likely composer of this piece, and give a reason for your answer.

Chopin   Bach   Schubert   Verdi   (1)

Reason: .... (1)

5 Look at the extract printed opposite, which is from the overture to *Die Fledermaus* by Johann Strauss, and then answer the questions below.

   (a) Give the meaning of:

       pizz. (e.g. bar 2, second violins) .... (2)

       a 2 (e.g. bar 6, clarinets) .... (2)

   (b) (i) Write out the parts for clarinets in bars 5–9 as they would sound at concert pitch.

(5)

      (ii) Write out the parts for horns in bars 14–15 as they would sound at concert pitch.

(3)

   (c) Complete the following statements:

      (i) A percussion instrument that plays later in the movement is the tamburo, which means

        .... (2)

      (ii) The opening phrase (bracketed) played by the solo oboe is repeated without the upbeat

        by the .... and the .... in bars .... (3)

   (d) Mark **clearly** on the score, using the appropriate capital letter for identification, one example of each of the following. Also give the bar number(s) of each of your answers, as shown in the answer to **A**.

      A   a place where the first violins are instructed to play a
          note loud then immediately soft (circle the note concerned). Bar ...14...

      B   the harmonic interval of a compound augmented 4th (augmented 11th)
          sounding between two double-reed instruments (circle the notes concerned). Bar .... (2)

      C   a place where the cellos and bassoons play
          the melodic interval of a minor 2nd in unison. Bar(s) .... (2)

      D   a place where the cellos play at a higher pitch than the violas. Bar .... (2)

      E   a place where the second violins have to play
          an open string (circle the note concerned). Bar .... (2)

BLANK PAGE

Theory Paper Grade 6   2008   C

TOTAL MARKS
100

Duration 3 hours

Candidates should answer all FIVE questions.
Write your answers on this paper – no others will be accepted.
Answers must be written clearly and neatly – otherwise marks may be lost.

1 Answer **ONE** section only, (a) or (b).

15

EITHER

(a) Indicate **ONE** chord at each of the places marked ∗ to accompany the following melody. You may do so by writing roman numerals or any other recognized method of notation between the staves, **OR** by writing notes on the staves which provide a proper harmonic structure; but use only **ONE** of these methods.

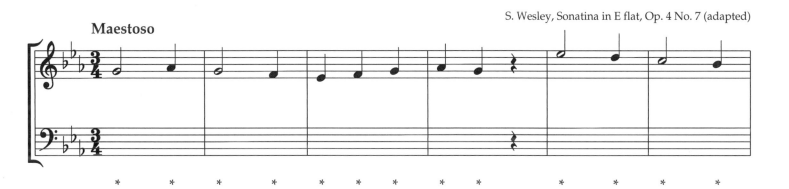

S. Wesley, Sonatina in E flat, Op. 4 No. 7 (adapted)

OR

(b) Complete the bass line and add a suitable figured bass as necessary, *from the first beat of bar 3*, at the places marked ∗ in this passage. If you wish to use a $\frac{5}{3}$ chord, leave the space under the asterisk blank, but $\frac{5}{3}$ chords *must* be shown when used as part of a $\frac{6}{4}\frac{5}{3}$ progression or when chromatic alteration is required.

2 Writing for four-part voices (SATB) or keyboard, realize this figured bass. Assume that all chords are $\frac{5}{3}$ unless otherwise shown.

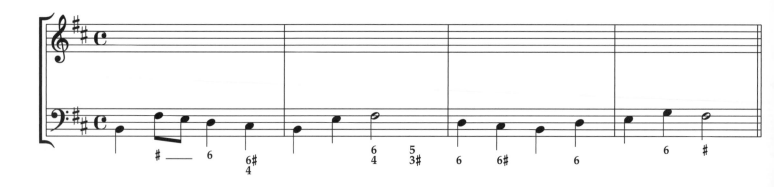

3 EITHER

(a) Continue this opening to form a complete melody for unaccompanied violin. It should end with a modulation to the relative minor and should be between eight and ten bars long. Add performance directions as appropriate and write the complete melody on the staves below.

OR

(b) Continue this opening for unaccompanied trombone to make a complete piece of not less than eight bars in length. You may make any modulation or modulations that you wish, or none if you prefer. Add performance directions as appropriate and write the complete melody on the staves below.

Tempo I [Andante con moto]

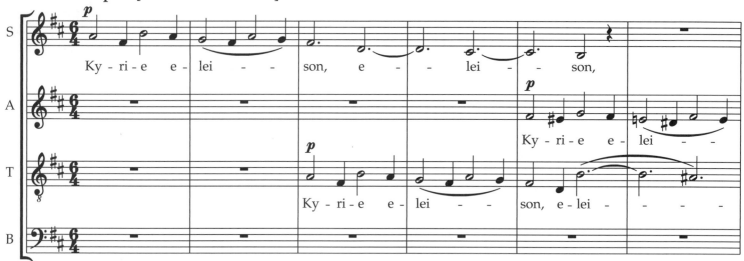

4 Look at the extract printed opposite, which is from Dvořák's Mass in D, and then answer the questions below.

(a) Complete the following statements:

 (i) The largest melodic interval in the tenor part is a(n) .... (2)

 (ii) A male voice pitched between tenor and bass is called a .... (2)

 (iii) The soprano note D in bar 10 is a note of melodic decoration (e.g. changing note) called

 a(n) .... (2)

(b) Identify the chords marked ∗ in bars 8 and 15 by writing on the dotted lines below. Use either words or symbols. Indicate the position of each chord, show whether it is major, minor, augmented or diminished, and name the prevailing key in bar 15.

Bar 8   ....   Key B minor (3)

Bar 15   ....   Key .... (4)

(c) Mark **clearly** on the score, using the appropriate capital letter for identification, one example of each of the following. Also give the bar number of each of your answers, as shown in the answer to **A**.

From bar 6 onwards

A a place where the tenors begin their loudest phrase. Bar ....10....

B a place where the tenors sing a note that sounds higher than the note the altos sing on

 the same beat (circle the notes concerned). Bar .... (2)

C the harmonic interval of a diminished 7th sounding between the alto and bass voices

 (circle the notes concerned). Bar .... (2)

D a place where the tenor and bass voices sing a note in unison (circle the notes concerned).

 Bar .... (2)

E the melodic interval of a diminished 3rd (circle the notes concerned). Bar .... (2)

(d) Answer TRUE or FALSE to each of the following statements:

 (i) The style of writing in bars 1–10 is polyphonic (contrapuntal). .... (2)

 (ii) The soprano and tenor voices never sing a note that sounds in unison. .... (2)

5 Look at the extract printed on pages 25–26 and then answer the questions below.

(a) Compare the opening phrase (bracketed) played by the first violins with its next appearance in bars 2–4. Apart from the fact that it is now played by a different instrument, give two reasons why it sounds different.

1 .... (1)

2 .... (1)

(b) (i) In this extract, the parts for clarinets are in C. On the first of the two blank staves at the foot of page 26, write out the part for first clarinet in bars 10–12 as it would appear for clarinet *in B♭*. (4)

(ii) Using the second of the blank staves at the foot of page 26, rewrite bars 10–11 of the first bassoon part so that it sounds at the same pitch but using the bass clef. (2)

(c) Identify the chord marked ✳ in bar 9 *in the woodwind parts* by writing on the dotted lines below. Use either words or symbols. Indicate the position of the chord, show whether it is major, minor, augmented or diminished, and name the prevailing key.

Chord .... Key .... (4)

(d) Mark **clearly** on the score, using the appropriate capital letter for identification, one example of each of the following. Also give the bar number(s) of each of your answers, as shown in the answer to **A**.

In bars 1–10 (first beat)

A the melodic interval of a major 7th (circle the notes concerned). Bar ....²....

B a place where a string player must play
    an open string (circle the note concerned). Bar .... (2)

C the harmonic interval of an augmented 2nd sounding between
    two different woodwind instruments (circle the notes concerned). Bar .... (2)

From bar 10 (second beat) onwards

D a place where violas and second bassoon sound two
    consecutive crotchet notes in unison (circle the notes concerned). Bar(s) .... (2)

E the harmonic interval of a minor 6th sounding between two
    different double-reed instruments (circle the notes concerned). Bar .... (2)

(e) Complete the following statement:

The figure formed from the four notes played by the violas and cellos at the beginning of

this extract is played again at a different pitch beginning in bar 13 by the .... ,

the .... and the .... (3)

(f) From the list below, underline the name of the most likely composer of this piece.

Rachmaninoff   Bach   Beethoven   Debussy   (2)

24

(b) (i)

Clarinet 1, bars 10–12

(b) (ii)

Bassoon 1, bars 10–11

Theory Paper Grade 6   2008   S

TOTAL MARKS
100

Duration 3 hours

Candidates should answer all FIVE questions.
Write your answers on this paper – no others will be accepted.
Answers must be written clearly and neatly – otherwise marks may be lost.

1 Answer **ONE** section only, (a) or (b).

15

EITHER

(a) Indicate **ONE** chord at each of the places marked ∗ to accompany the following melody. You may do so by writing roman numerals or any other recognized method of notation between the staves, **OR** by writing notes on the staves which provide a proper harmonic structure; but use only **ONE** of these methods.

Melody by Milgrove (adapted)

OR

(b) Complete the bass line and add a suitable figured bass as necessary, *from the first beat of bar 4*, at the places marked * in this passage. If you wish to use a $\frac{5}{3}$ chord, leave the space under the asterisk blank, but $\frac{5}{3}$ chords *must* be shown when used as part of a $\frac{6}{4}\frac{5}{3}$ progression or when chromatic alteration is required.

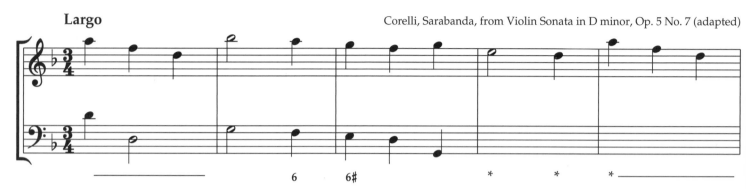

2 Writing for four-part voices (SATB) or keyboard, realize this figured bass.
  Assume that all chords are $\frac{5}{3}$ unless otherwise shown.

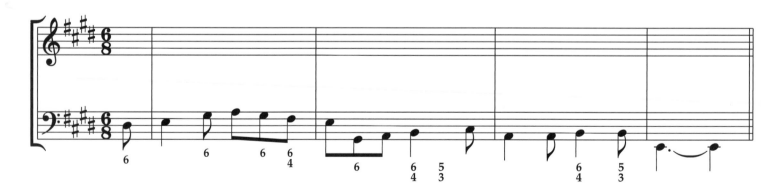

3 EITHER

(a) Continue this opening to form a complete melody for unaccompanied bassoon. It should end with a modulation to the relative major and should be between eight and ten bars long. Add performance directions as appropriate and write the complete melody on the staves below.

Allegro

Spohr (adapted)

OR

(b) Continue this opening for unaccompanied violin to make a complete piece of not less than eight bars in length. You may make any modulation or modulations that you wish, or none if you prefer. Add performance directions as appropriate and write the complete melody on the staves below.

Andante grazioso

4 Look at the extract printed opposite, which is from the third movement of C. P. E. Bach's ⬚25⬚ Sonata in D minor for keyboard, and then answer the questions below.

(a) Identify the chords marked ＊ in bars 1 and 9 by writing on the dotted lines below. Use either words or symbols. For each chord indicate the position, show whether it is major, minor, augmented or diminished, and name the prevailing key.

Bar 1 .... Key .... (4)

Bar 9 .... Key .... (4)

(b) Give the full name (e.g. note of anticipation) of each of the numbered and circled notes of melodic decoration in the right-hand part.

1 (bar 2, E)   .... (2)

2 (bar 16, F♯)   .... (2)

3 (bar 22, B♮)   .... (2)

(c) Write out in full the right-hand part of bar 9 as you think it should be played.

(3)

(d) Mark **clearly** on the score, using the appropriate capital letter for identification, one example of each of the following. Also give the bar number(s) of each of your answers, as shown in the answer to **A**.

In bars 1–8

A the harmonic interval of a major 3rd in
   the left-hand part (circle the notes concerned). Bar .....5....

B the melodic interval of an augmented 2nd in
   the right-hand part (circle the notes concerned). Bar .... (2)

C an ascending chromatic semitone (augmented unison)
   in the left-hand part (circle the notes concerned). Bar .... (2)

D an example of syncopation. Bar .... (2)

From bar 9 onwards

E a two-bar melodic sequence (not exact) which
   begins a semitone higher than the previous two bars. Bars .... (2)

5 Look at the extract printed opposite and then answer the questions below.

(a) Give the meaning of:

a 2 (clarinets, bar 1) .... (2)

arco (bar 1) .... (2)

 (e.g. second violins, bar 1) .... (2)

senza sord. (first violins, bar 7) .... (2)

(b) (i) Write out the parts for clarinets in bars 5–8 as they would sound at concert pitch.

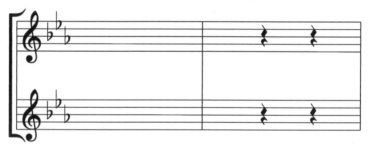

(4)

(ii) Write out the parts for horns in bars 7–8 as they would sound at concert pitch.

(4)

(c) Complete the following statements:

(i) A standard orchestral double-reed instrument that does *not* play in this extract is the

.... (2)

(ii) Two members of the standard orchestral brass family that do *not* play in this extract are

the .... and the .... (2)

(iii) A standard orchestral woodwind instrument, *not* playing here, that sounds an octave

higher than written is the .... (2)

(iv) The bracketed harmonic interval sounding between the first bassoon and the second

violins on the first beat of bar 7 is a(n) .... (2)

(d) From the list below, underline one period during which you think this piece was written.

1700–1800   1800–1900   1900–2000

(1)